D1192799

The Child
On His Knees

BY
MARY DIXON THAYER

Originally published in 1926 by the MacMillan
Company, NewYork. Printed in the United States of America.

Cover design by Joan Barger

ISBN# 0-912141-06-9

CMA Press
P.O. Box 255
Harrison, NY 10528

"How nice it was of You to be
A Little Child, dear God!

I love to think my feet are on
The same world that You trod!"

For all children, everywhere,
but especially for Molly.

CONTENTS

CONTENTS

6

CONTENTS

CONTENTS

THE CHILD
ON HIS KNEES

The Child on His Knees

IN THE MORNING

SEE, God! I make a little Prayer
For You, and through the golden air
Of morning let it fly away
Across the world, across Today,

Across the stars, and on, and on...
Look, God! It is already gone!
I cannot follow where it goes...
Nobody knows...nobody knows

But only You! God, take it, please
Just for a second on Your knees
And comfort it—a tiny Prayer
Is so afraid of Everywhere!

God, do You think that You could smile
And play with it—a little while?
O! If You only will, I'll try
To send you others, bye and bye!

THE CHILD ON HIS KNEES

IN CHURCH

O! HERE I am, dear God,
Kneeling at Your throne,
And I know that I am not
Kneeling here alone!

For I know that Angels
All around must be,
With their white wings folded,
And their eyes on me.

Yes! There is an Angel
Always in this place,
Kneeling at Your altar
And hiding his face...

God, I know that You are
Here because of me,
And I feel Your nearness,
Though I cannot see...

THE CHILD ON HIS KNEES

And I kneel and whisper
"God! I love You so!"
And the Angels pass me
Softly, tippy-toe...

SPRING PRAYER

WHAT do You think, dear God?
Down in the woods I found
A flower dressed in blue
Coming out of the ground!

What do You think, dear God?
Today I saw a tree
All full of baby leaves
Shaking their heads at me!

What do You think, dear God?
I picked a buttercup!
And underneath my feet
A little star looked up!

O! Thank You, God, for all
This lovely time of year!
Thank You for everything
That You have done down here!

SUMMER PRAYER

WHAT fun it is to be a child
upon a summer's day!
O God, You know what fun it is
To be a child and play!

The sky is a blue china bowl,
And in it the clouds float,
And one is like a big white Swan
With a long, curly throat!

And one is like an old, old Man
With a grey beard, and there
Is one just like a Lady with
A veil around her hair!

O God! What fun it is to lie
Upon a hill and look
At pictures in the sky, instead
Of in a silly book!

THE CHILD ON HIS KNEES

O God! What fun it is to hear
The daisies talking to
The wind, as he comes running by,
And says, "how do you do?"...

AUTUMN PRAYER

THE leaves are dressed in red and gold,
And they come floating far...
They look like Fairies—and I think
Perhaps some of them are!

Dear God, I know a little path
All covered soft and deep
With Fairies—dressed in red and gold—
All fallen fast asleep!

I know a place where Angels come,
With folded wings, to pray...
At least, I think they do—I think
I saw one there today!

At any rate, dear God, it is
The sort of place, You know,
That Angels would be in if they
Could choose where they would go.

THE CHILD ON HIS KNEES

I like to run down there and say
My prayers, dear God! I kneel
Upon the ground, and look around,
And then I seem to feel

The Angels moving softly on
The grass, and Trees lean down,
And whisper, "Say a prayer for us!"
Sometimes they put their brown

Arms gently round me, whispering
"O pray for us—O pray!"
And so I do, dear God, You know
The Prayer for Trees I say—

The one that asks You please to give
Them lots of birds to sing
Among their branches, and a lot
Of new leaves in the Spring...

And snow to keep them warm when their
Bare legs begin to freeze,
And all the rain they want, dear God!
That is my Prayer for Trees.

WINTER PRAYER

THE world is covered up with snow
Today, dear God! I want to go

And play in it before the sun
Comes out and melts it. O! What fun

It is to be a child today!
"Thank You!" Is all that I can say!

"Thank You, dear God, for trees that stand
And shine like trees in Fairyland!

Thank You for the blue of the sky!
Thank you for a cloud going by!"

Dear God, this is my Winter Prayer—
"Thank You for snow-flakes, everywhere!"

THE CHILD ON HIS KNEES

EARLY PRAYER

GOD, please make me good today
When I work and when I play!

It is easy, God, You see,
For a little child like me

To forget You always know
What I think, and where I go,

How I act, and that You're sad
Every single time I'm bad!

O! Please make me good today
When I work and when I play!

LATE PRAYER

DEAR God! How beautiful are all
The stars! I know that they would fall

Unless You kept them where they are.
I know, dear God, that every star

Goes only where You tell it to,
And does what it is meant to do.

O! When I look up at the sky,
Sometimes it almost makes me cry

To think that even stars obey
You better than I do each day!

A WISH

O! I OFTEN wish
That I really could
Always only do
As You wish I would!
O! I wish that I
Loved You, God the way
You ought to be loved!
I will try, today.

TO OUR LADY

LOVELY Lady dressed in blue—
Teach me how to pray!
God was just your little Boy,
Tell me what to say!
Did you lift Him up, sometimes,
Gently, on your knee?
Did you sing to Him the way
Mother does to me?
Did you hold His hand at night?
Did you ever try
Telling stories of the world?
O! And did He cry?
Do you really think He cares
If I tell Him things—
Little things that happen? And
Do the Angels' wings
Make a noise? And can He hear
Me if I speak low?

THE CHILD ON HIS KNEES

Does He understand me now?
Tell me—for you know!
Lovely Lady dressed in blue,
Teach me how to pray!
God was just your little Boy.
And you know the way.

AFTERWARDS

WHEN the "Our Father" I have said,
And mother tucks me into bed,
And kisses me, and calls "Good-night,
God bless you!" And turns out the
    light—
Why, then I lie awake and say
Another prayer a diff'rent way.
I talk to God, and Angels keep
Their wings around me till I sleep.
I talk to God and tell Him things
All in between the Angels' wings,
And God leans down and says "I know.
I understand. I love you so!"

THE CHILD ON HIS KNEES

THE LITTLE PRAYER

SOME of the prayers I ought to know
Have words that are so long
I can't remember what they are,
Or where they all belong.
And then I feel like crying, God,
For I suppose I should
Know all those prayers by heart—and O!
I do want to be good!
But mother says You understand
That I am very small,
And that You like it if I pray
In my own words and all...
Now, when I cannot think just how
A prayer is meant to go,
I kneel down anyway and say
"Dear God, I love you so!"

THANKSGIVING

I WANT to thank You first of all,
Dear God, for making me,
Because—if I had not been made—
Goodness! Where *would* I be?
And then I want to thank You, God,
For my dearest mother—
O! I'm glad I have her, God,
Instead of another!
And then I want to thank You for
My father and the boys,
And for my sisters too, and for
Our house, and for our toys!
And God, I want to thank You for
The lovely, lovely sky,
And for the clouds that way, way up
Above the world go by!
And God, I want to thank You for
The woods in which we play,

And for the stars and moon by night,
And for the sun by day...
And God, I want to thank You for
The daisy-fields, and hills
Made to coast down in Winter-time,
And have the finest spills!
And God, I want to thank You for
All sorts of little things—
Like curly stems of dandelions,
And pebbles, and the wings
Of butterflies, and icicles,
And leaves, and bugs that pass—
O! And for diamonds that I find
Each morning in the grass!
Dear God, there are a million things
To thank You for, I know!
I haven't thought of half of them—
For instance, there is snow...
But God, I don't believe I can

THE CHILD ON HIS KNEES

Remember all that I
Have got to thank You for, and so
I don't believe I'll try.
But God—You know the way I feel—
I mean I love You, and
O! Thank you just for everything!
There! *Now* you understand!

DO YOU REALLY?

GOD, when I have been very bad—
Then have I really made You sad?
And do You really, *truly* care
What I do always, everywhere?
O Yes! I know You do, for I
Know that You came on earth to try
And teach us how to work and play
And how never to disobey;
And how if You had not cared for me
You would not have come down to be
A child here in the world, and die.
You would have stayed up in the sky!

FINDING YOU

DEAR God, I wish I could have been
  Among those girls and boys
You called to come and talk to You,
And who left all their toys,
And ran and climbed up on Your knee,
And held Your hand, and sat
Around You, learning lovely things—
I wish I had done that!
But God, I know that even now
I can get close to You.
I know that You still love children—yes
Indeed! I know You do!
And so I often slip away
Into the Church, and kneel
Down at the altar where You are,
And tell You all I feel.
I cannot see Your face, and yet

THE CHILD ON HIS KNEES

I know that You are there.
I know I'm just as close to You
As all those children were!

AN INVITATION

I CAN'T think why You love me, God!
And yet I know You do!
I know You want me, when I die,
To come and live with You!

KNOWING

I KNOW wherever I may be
That God is looking down at me.
I know He made the earth and sky,
And that the stars come spinning by
Just like big tops! (He makes them go
Like that) O Yes! And then I know
That really nothing is too small
For God to love. I know that all
The flowers on the hills are dear
To Him as stars, and that down here
Upon the world if I am bad—
Why! Even I can make God sad!

THE CHILD ON HIS KNEES

FIRST COMMUNION

IT'S almost time! Dear God, I kneel
And wait for You to come! I feel
A tiny bit afraid—but O!
I love You, and of course You know
I do, and yet You like to hear
Me say how much when You are near.
Dear God, I love You more than I
Can tell—but O! Before I die—
I want to love You more than now!
So, won't You come and show me how?

THE CHILD ON HIS KNEES

AFTER COMMUNION

DEAR God, dear God, You came to me!
How glad I am! And yet I see
I am not what I ought to be.
Here is my heart! It's small, but I
Have filled it up with love. I'll try
To keep it that way 'till I die.

LEARNING

WHEN You were little, God, I know
You never, never did
What wasn't nice, or anything
Your Mother might forbid.
When You were little, God, I know
You didn't hide or cry
When bedtime came—and O! I know
You *never* told a lie!
When You were little, God, I know
If other little boys
Arrived to play and took away
Or broke Your dearest toys—
You didn't call them names and wish
They hadn't come at all.
O! Won't You teach me how to be
Like You when You were small?

BEING TAUGHT

DEAR God, I want to always do
The very best I can
To please You now I am a child,
And when I am a man.
And though I love You lots today,
I want to love You more
Tomorrow than today or than
I ever have before!

THE CHILD ON HIS KNEES

HOW NICE!

HOW nice it is, dear God, to know
That You make all the flowers grow!
How nice it is to stop and think
You made the spring from which I drink!
How nice it is to know that You
Painted the sky that lovely blue!
How nice it is to know You fill
The night with stars and always will!
But O! How nice to know You made
Me, too! Sometimes I am afraid
I do not thank You as I should—
You are so wise, dear God, and good!

WISHING

SOMETIMES I really almost hear
My Guardian Angel's wings,
And sometimes, God, You come so near—
So near—and whisper things!
I can't quite see You, but I know
When You lean over me—
O! Then I wish I were as good
As a child ought to be!

THE CHILD ON HIS KNEES

PERHAPS HE WON'T

PEOPLE in Church walk quietly,
  And sometimes shake their heads at me
  Very—O! Very solemnly!
  Of course I know that God is there
  And that I mustn't talk or stare
  Or laugh or wiggle during prayer.
  But I know that God used to be
  A little Child himself, and He
  Won't mind if I am fidgety
  In Church, perhaps, if only I
  Say all my prayers, and really try
  To be a Saint before I die.

GIVING BACK

I HAVE so many lovely things
That seem to be my own,
But it was You who gave them all,
Dear God, and when I'm grown
Please show me how to give them back
In other ways to You—
Please show me how to give You all
I have in all I do.

I KNOW

DEAR God, I know, although I'm small,
That everything I do—
Yes—even everything I think—
Matters a lot to You!
I know, although I am so small,
That I am just as dear
To You as bigger people are,
And can come just as near.
O God! Why do You love me so?
There is no reason why...
O Please! I want to love You more
Each day until I die.

PLANS

WHEN I grow up I want to be
   A Saint because I know, You see,
   That that will please You, God,
      more than
   If I am just a Famous Man.
   (Of course I may be Famous too—
   I really don't know *what* I'll do...)
   But God, whatever I decide,
   Please keep me always at Your side!

WHY DO YOU CARE?

DEAR God, why do You care so much
If I am good or bad?
Why do You ever let me make
You sorry, God, or glad?
If I were You it seems to me
I wouldn't mind at all
What children do because You see,
We really are so small.
But God, I know that what I do
And think and everything
Is just as serious to You
As if I were a King!
So please don't let me act as if
I thought You didn't care—
I know You do—and O! I hope
That You will hear this Prayer!

HOPES

I HOPE, dear God, that all I say
And do, and think, at work or play,
Will bring me nearer You each day.
O God! I want to get as near
To You as I can get, down here!

I LOVE YOU

I LOVE YOU GOD! And I want to
Tell You forever that I do!
Please make my life into a Song
That sings *"I love You"* all day long!
I love You, God! How can I say
The same thing in a different way?
But then I know You do not mind
Although I cannot seem to find
New words to put into a Prayer—
I love You, God! And everywhere
I go, and in all that I do
I send my love, dear God, to You!

JUST THINK!

I'M GLAD, dear God, that when You came
Down on the world to die,
You were a little Child at first—
No bigger than am I!
Just think! You were a Child so that
All other children could
Remember what You did, and learn
From You how to be good!
Just think! You might have floated down
From Heaven on a star!
You might have been a King the way
In Heaven, now, You are!
Just think! You might have come to us
Already tall and old—

THE CHILD ON HIS KNEES

You might have been so strict, and *made*
Us do as we were told!
Just think! And yet, instead, You came
Down as a Child and played
With other children, and You had
A mother You obeyed.
Thank You, dear God! For now I know
You understand the way
It feels to be a child and have
Big People to obey.

FORGIVE ME

DEAR God, sometimes I feel so small,
And You seem so far off, and all!
Sometimes I think "O dear, O dear,
Why can't I do as I want here?"
And sometimes, when I kneel to pray,
My mind is not on what I say.
Dear God! Forgive me when I act
Like that—when I am bad, in fact!

THE CHILD ON HIS KNEES

PERHAPS...

DEAR God, I wonder, when You climbed
The hill of Calvary—
Where were the children that You used
To take upon Your knee?
Where were they? In among the crowd?
And did they, too, not care
What happened to You God, dear God,
But only came to stare?
Where were the children that You loved?
They do not seem to be
Around as You begin to climb
The hill of Calvary!
O God I wish that I had been
A child that day! I might
Have done some little thing for You
To make the Cross more light!

THE CHILD ON HIS KNEES

I might have given You a glass
Of water on the way—
I might have whispered, as You passed,
"I love You so today!"
I might have done this—and yet—O!
Perhaps I would have hid
Among the people and done just
What other children did?

A GIFT

TAKE all of me today, dear God!
I want to give You all
I think and do and say and am,
From morning till nightfall!
I want to live for You today!
I want to try and fill
The minutes up with love for You—
And O! I hope I will!

THE CHILD ON HIS KNEES

WHEN YOU WERE LITTLE

WHEN You were just a little Boy,
Dear God, I know that You
Did what You were told, and never
Said anything untrue.
When You were just a little Boy,
Dear God, I think, maybe,
Your Mother scolded You sometimes
The way mine does with me?
And yet I know that You, dear God,
Did not deserve it when
This happened, but You never cried,
Or answered her back then.
O God! I want to be the sort
Of Child You were—I'll try
To do as I am told, and not
To answer back, or cry.

OF COURSE

DEAR God, I know You used to be
A little child on earth, like me.
When I am naughty I will try
To think of You, and not to cry.
And when I want to disobey
I'll run to You instead, and pray.
Now that I know You used to be
A little child on earth—like me—
I know You must have understood
How hard it is to be so good!

FORGETTING

WHEN you are small—like me—it is
So very easy to
Forget your prayers, or say them
without thinking—when you do!
The world is such a great big place
To be in when you're small,
And everything that's in it is
So wonderful, and all!
Sometimes, dear God, I do not think
Of You the live-long day—
I only think what fun it is
To be a child and play!
I only think what fun it is
To be a child and know
All sorts of lovely things (like where
The yellow violets grow.
And bluebells, and those little, sad
White flowers that I love—

THE CHILD ON HIS KNEES

Or where a robin builds his nest—
Or maybe it's a dove...)
I know so many things like that,
You see—just heaps of things!
Why, only just today I found
A bug with spotty wings!
But God, I know You made the world,
And all that's in it, and
How I forget You ever, I
Just *cannot* understand!

THE THING TO DO

TO PLEASE You, God, I know that I
Need not do anything but try
To be as good as I can be
Because You lived and died for me.

THE ANSWER

WHY do You hide from us, dear God?
I often wish that I
Could see You now, and did not have
To wait until I die!
But O! I know the reason that
You hide from us is clear—
You are too beautiful, dear God,
For us to see You here.

PLEASE!

GOD, please make me love You more
Than I ever have before!
I know that You used to be
Just a little child like me—
I know You came all the way
Down from Heaven, Christmas Day,
Just to show You love us so.
O Yes, God! I know! I know!
So I want to love You more
Than I ever have before.

WORDS

EVERYTHING speaks of You, dear God!
The clouds up in the sky
Tell me about You as they pass,
And the wind, going by,
Whispers "He sent me!" On the hills
The grasses softly say
"We know Him too!" And all the trees
Stand still, and try to pray.
Everything speaks of You! The sun,
As it comes up, calls out
"O! See how beautiful I am!
He made me!" And the shout
Goes all around the world, dear God—
"He made me—see! O see!"
And in the night-time all the stars
Keep saying it to me.
Yes! Everywhere I go, dear God

THE CHILD ON HIS KNEES

And everywhere I look
Things speak to me of You, and tell
Me more than any book.
O God! I've learned such lovely things
About You from a rose!
And O! I know that You have taught
A lily how to close!
And O! I know that You have painted all
The flowers on the hills—
And so I think of You, of You—
When I see daffodils!

MESSAGES

HOW can I love You more, dear God?
I really do not know!
  And yet I want to love You more!
  O Please—do come and show
  Me how! I want to love You, God,
  So much that everything
  Will speak to me of You—so much
  That all the birds will sing
  Of You, and all the flowers of
  The world will look at me
  And nod "We love Him too!" And trees
  Say softly "So do we..."
  Dear God! Please let me love You so
  That even little things—
  Like leaves, and petals, and the gold
  Splash on butterfly-wings,
  And drops of rain, and little fires

THE CHILD ON HIS KNEES

Of dew upon the grass,
And little fists of baby ferns,
And little winds that pass
Will tell me lovely secrets. God,
They all know about You—
O! If I listen, I will learn
So much! But it is true
I sometimes do not listen, and
I simply go along
And do not ask about You, God,
And I know that is wrong.
For if I really love You—why!
The whole wide world will bring
Me messages from You—You'll write
Me notes on everything!

THE LONELY FEELING

I AM so lonely, God, for You
Sometimes! It seems to me
You are so far away, and O!
I wish that I could see
You now, and hold Your hand, and look
Up in Your face, and smile—
I wish that I could hear You talk,
Dear God, once in a while!
But after all I know, of course,
That when a person dies
He finds himself right at the door
Of Your house—Paradise!
And You will say "Come in! Come in!
What are you waiting for?
My child, I love you—and you won't
Be lonely anymore."

COMING BACK

SOMETIMES dear God, when I've been bad,
  I am afraid to pray—
  I feel as if You were so sad
  I'd better stay away.
  I feel as if You couldn't want
  Me ever close to You—
  I feel as if You never could
  Forgive the things I do.
  But O! I know You said that if
  We really, truly try
  Not to be bad again, You will
  Forgive us, and so I
  Come back to You each time and say
  "Dear God! Look what I did!
  I'm sorry, God. Please help me to
  Not do what You forbid."

THE MAIN THING

O! PEOPLE sometimes use such long
Words when they talk of You,
  I don't know what they mean, dear God,
  Although big people do.
  But then of course the thing that I
  Need most of all to know
  Is that You came down on the world
  To live, awhile ago,
  And You did this because You love
  Us so, and wish that we
  Would learn how to be good the way
  We really ought to be.

THE CHILD ON HIS KNEES

I THINK

DEAR God, You are so very kind
I think You really do not mind
Although I cannot always pray
To You in the most solemn way.
I think You really like to hear
The little things that happen here,
And so I tell you everything,
And You are always listening.
I often ask You please to make
Me much, much better when I wake,
And then I ask You please to keep
Your arms around me while I sleep,
Because I know I'm very small
Compared to the Angels and all—
But then I know You used to say
"Let all the little children stay
Close, close to me!" You did not scold

THE CHILD ON HIS KNEES

"Send them back later—when they're old!"
O no! You said "Come close to Me!"
And that is where I want to be!

SOMETIMES

SOMETIMES it is so easy to
Just kneel right down and pray,
Or do it standing up, or while
I am at school, or play.
But other times, dear God, You know
It's very hard indeed—
My head gets full of lots of things
It really doesn't need.
And when I try to think of You,
And when I try to pray,
Why! Then I find the thoughts inside
My head are in the way!
I think of silly little things
Instead, dear God, of You.
I think of silly things to say,
And silly things to do.
And O! Although I try and try
To think of what I should,

THE CHILD ON HIS KNEES

The thoughts inside my head jump up
And say "I *won't* be good!"
But even if they will not all
Behave, You are so kind
That if I'm sorry, God, dear God,
Perhaps You do not mind?

LOVING

I LOVE so many people, God!
In fact, I think that I
Love everybody in the world!
And O! I often try
To make them love me too. I like
To have them smile at me,
And say "What a nice child that is!
Delicious, isn't she?"
But God, I know I shouldn't care
So much what people say,
For sometimes I am bad although
I do not look that way.
Dear God, I know You want me to
Love people, but I know
I ought to love You most of all
Of course, dear God, and so
When I love anybody I

The Child on His Knees

Will bring him right to You
And say "Look, God! This is my friend!
Please keep our friendship true!"

THE CHILD ON HIS KNEES

HOW KIND!

HOW kind of You, dear God, to let
Children come crowding 'round You yet!
How kind of You to make us feel
You really like it when we kneel
Close, close to You! O! Everyday
I try to go to Church and pray!
I know that You are everywhere,
Dear God, but You are closer there.
When You were in the world You said
"This is My Body," of the bread.
It's hard to understand, but You
Would never say what isn't true!

A THOUGHT

ALL that I do—no matter what—
If it is done for love
Will be a sort of Prayer of Thanks
To You, dear God, above!

THINKING

G OD, when I do not think of You—
When I forget to pray—
I cannot tell if I am near
To You or far away.
O God! Please let me always see
How far I am from You!
Please show me what I ought to be,
And what I ought to do!

THE CHILD ON HIS KNEES

FOR YOU

I DO NOT only pray, dear God,
When I am on my knees,
But while I work and while I play—
Yes, all day long! O Please—
I want to love You more and more,
And whatever I do
Do well just for Your sake, dear God!
Haven't You asked me to?

THE CHILD ON HIS KNEES

IF I SHOULD DIE

IF I SHOULD die today, dear God,
I don't believe I'd mind.
I know You love me very much,
And that You're very kind.
I know that if I have been good
There is no reason why
I shouldn't see You right away,
Dear God, if I should die.

THE CHILD ON HIS KNEES

AT NIGHT

HELP me, dear God, to live the way
You want me to live day by day.
   O! Show me how to please You best
When I'm at work, or play, or rest!
And may I often think of You,
And never say what isn't true,
And never do what isn't right—
I think that's all, dear God,
   Goodnight!

THE CHILD ON HIS KNEES

TO THE BLESSED MOTHER

MOTHER, I want to always be
Your child. Will you take care of me?
When God was just a little Boy
I know He gave you lots of joy;
And if He later made you sad,
I know that now He makes you glad.
And I believe if a child dies
That, when he gets to Paradise,
If you'll just touch God's hand and say
"O *Please* don't send that child away!"
God will say softly "Mother dear,
You can have all you ask for here!"

THE STAIRS

I LIKE to think the days are steps
On which You've set my feet,
   And I must climb them one by one,
   Dear God, until we meet.

THE CHILD ON HIS KNEES

AT PLAY

OFTEN, dear God, when I'm at play
I think of You, and then I say
"I love You, God!" It only takes
A second—but it always makes
Me happier to whisper this.
It's just as if I ran to kiss
You in between our games, and see
That You are smiling down at me.

WHEN I'M OLD

DEAR God, I hope that when I'm old
I can look back and say
"I tried to know You better and
To love You more each day."
And O! I hope that when I'm old
I can give You my hand,
And whisper "Ready, God!" and that
You'll smile, and understand.

THE CHILD ON HIS KNEES

THOUGHTS

I WANT to think of You, dear God,
A million times a day—
At home, and when I am in school,
And when I am at play!
No matter who is by, nor where
I am, nor what I do,
I know that I can always send
A thought, dear God, to You!

THE CHILD ON HIS KNEES

IF...

I WILL not keep my love for You
Locked up inside my heart.
I will not hide it there, dear God,
From all the world apart!
O no! I want to love You so
That this heart never will
Be able to hold all my love,
And then it soon must spill
Into the hearts of everyone
I meet, and O! I know
That if I really love You, God,
It's sure to happen so!

The Child on His Knees

NOW
OF COURSE it will be easy, God,
To love You when I see
You face to face in Heaven and
You put Your arms 'round me!
It will be easy then, of course,
To love You as I should—
But O! While I can't see You, it
Is harder to be good!
Dear God, You know how hard it is
Because You tried it too—
You came down on the world to teach
Us what we ought to do.
You know it's hard to act as if
I saw You everyday,
And yet, dear God, I know that You
Are near me when I pray.
I know that every single time
I think of You, You lean
Down out of Paradise to me,
And nothing comes between!

SOME CHILDREN

SOME children have so little, God,
Compared with me! And they
Are bad, perhaps, but then they have
Not ever learned to pray.
When I am bad it is so much,
Much worse because I take
All that You give me, and I know
That when I'm bad I make
You sad, dear God, and yet I go
And do wrong just the same—
O Yes! Sometimes I even put
On someone else the blame!
O! Show me how to use the things
You give, so You won't be
Too sorry that You gave them (out
Of all the world) to me!

THE CHILD ON HIS KNEES

WHAT WILL I DO?

WHEN I see You at last, dear God,
I wonder what You'll say?
I wonder if I'll feel ashamed
And want to run away?
I wonder, when I kneel, at last,
And look into Your eyes,
And all the Angels bow their heads
Up there in Paradise...
I wonder...will I feel ashamed
Because I didn't do
All that I might have done, dear God,
Down in the world, for you?
And even if You smile and take
My hand, dear God, will I
Be happy? Won't I want to hide
Away, somewhere—and cry?

THE CHILD ON HIS KNEES

TO THINK!

TO THINK You care, dear God, for me
Who really am so small!
To think that anything I do
Matters to You at all!
Why! All the Angels, looking on,
Must feel sad when they see
How little I love You compared
With how much You love me!
O! Show me how to love You more!
I want to love You, God!
I want to follow, through the world,
The same path that You trod!

WHAT I DO KNOW

I KNOW I'll never understand
(At least not till I die)
A lot of things, dear God, and yet
My head keeps asking "Why?"
Why do some people cry and wish
They never had been made?
Why are some people sick, dear God,
And hungry and afraid?
My head keeps asking "Why? Why?
Why?"
And yet, I understand
That I am much too little to
Know all that You have planned.
And after all, dear God, I know
When You were here You cried—
Like us—and You were poor, and You
Were laughed at, and You died!

THE CHILD ON HIS KNEES

PRESENTS

I THINK, dear God, the nicest prayer
Is thinking of You, everywhere!
All day long my heart keeps saying
"For You, God!" And that is praying.
So, out of all I think and do
I can make presents, God, for You.
O! I will always try to give
You lots of presents while I live!

THE CHILD ON HIS KNEES

THE FIRST PRESENT

ALL by myself I never can
Do anything that's fine.
But You will help me, God, if I
Give You all that is mine.
And so I give You everything
I have, and myself too,
And You can do with me, dear God,
Just as You want to do!

SOME DAYS

SOME days, dear God, You seem so near
I really almost feel
   You right beside me all the time,
   And when at night I kneel
   To say my prayers it seems as if
   I really ought to see
   You standing there beside the bed,
   Or leaning over me!
   But other times, dear God, You seem
   So far—so very far!
   And then I wonder if You hear
   My prayers, and where You are?
   And O! Then it is hard, You know,
   To pray the way I should—
   When You seem far away and I
   Don't feel like being good!
   Dear God, remind me every prayer

THE CHILD ON HIS KNEES

I ever say, You hear.
Remind me when You seem far off,
You *really* are quite near.

THE MISTAKE

THOUGH people sometimes look at me
And say nice things, and smile,
I know I'm not as good as I
May seem once in a while.
I know, dear God, that lots of times
I'm really very bad.
O! Lots of times, dear God, I know
I make You very sad!
Then why, I wonder, am I glad
When people smile at me
And think that I am nicer than
I am? I ought to be
Ashamed. I ought to tell them that
They have made a mistake—
And yet I don't! O no! I feel
Quite proud! Dear God, please make
Me really good! I do not want

THE CHILD ON HIS KNEES

To only be a sham.
Please make me good—or anyway
Much better than I am!

TRYING

DEAR God, I know that when I say
My prayers You always lean
Down out of heaven, and You know
Exactly what I mean.
O yes, dear God! I know You hear
All that I want to say—
Yes, even when the words get mixed up
In a most awful way!
Yes! Even when I think of lots
Of silly little things
Instead of only You, or Saints,
Or Angels with white wings—
Yes! Even then You always will
Forgive me, God, if I
Kneel down and say "I will be good"...
And really, truly try!

THE DIFFERENCE

I KNOW the world would not be half
    As lovely, God if You
  Had never come to live on it,
  And tell us what is true.
  Of course, even before You came,
  The flowers used to grow,
  And there were stars, and birds, and trees,
  And clouds, and wind and snow...
  (Perhaps there are some people yet
  Who think—before You came—
  That everything here in the world
  Was just about the same)
  O! But I know that all the world
  Is different, dear God,
  Since You came down to tell us that
  You love us—since You trod
  The world I'm very sure that all

THE CHILD ON HIS KNEES

The trees and flowers now
Are much, much prettier, dear God,
And when the big trees bow
Their heads, and the white faces of
The little stars look out
Or when the sun is shining and
The birds sing all about...
O! Everything is lovelier
Because You used to be
A Child here in the world, dear God—
A little Child—like me!

THE CHILD ON HIS KNEES

SO MUCH!

YOU love each one of us, dear God
Such a great deal, I know—
Such a great deal, You could not love
Us more—and even though
I were the only child upon
The world, dear God, You would
Have died for me—just me—to teach
Just me how to be good!

GROWING

IT SEEMS to me I really *don't*
Grow better day by day—
I'm naughty lots of times, dear God,
In every sort of way!
And yet I think I really ought
To be quite good by now,
For I am nearly ten, and You
Have told and told me how!
O! But I know I am not good
The way I ought to be,
In spite of all that You have done
Dear God, dear God for me!
You won't get tired—will You, God—
Of helping me? For I
Do want to please You and be good—
And O! I really try!

THE CHILD ON HIS KNEES

O DO!

S HOW me how to begin
To work for You, dear God!
Show me how to keep in
The little path You trod!

THE CHILD ON HIS KNEES

IF ONLY

I WISH I'd been a child, dear God,
When You were little too!
O! Think of all the lovely things
We would have thought to do!
Perhaps I would have lived across
The street, and everyday
Perhaps You would have asked me to
Come over, God, and play?
Perhaps You would have taught me how
To saw up wood or clean
The shop or build a little house?—
What fun *that* would have been!
And then perhaps when we had worked
At that for quite a while,
You Mother would have come right in

THE CHILD ON HIS KNEES

And kissed us with a smile!
O! If I'd only been a child
When You were little too!
Just *think*, dear God, of all the things
We would have thought to do!

A PUZZLE

HOW can I really, truly want
To please You, and yet be
  As naughty as I am sometimes?
  O God, I do not see!

COMFORT

I AM SO very little, God!
What can You do with me?
I don't see how what is so small
Of any use can be!
O! But I know You do not care
If I am big or small—
You only ask me for my heart,
Dear God, my heart—that's all!

PEOPLE

THE loveliest people are always
The people who keep just as near
To You, dear God, as they can—and so
Of course it is quite, quite clear
That the reason I love these people
(And everyone knows it is true)
Is that all these people are lovely
Because they're in love with You!

THE CHILD ON HIS KNEES

WAKING UP

A S SOON as I wake up, I say
"Please help me, God, to live today
For You—just You!" And then I pray
A little while in my own way.
And when I get up out of bed
Such lovely thoughts are in my head!
I feel all sort of comforted!
I *know* I'll see You when I'm dead!

IF I WERE YOU

YES dear God! I know You love me!
And yet I can't see why!
It seems to me if I were You
I wouldn't even try.
It seems to me if I were You
I'd simply say "O well,
Why should I bother what they do
Down on the world?" I'd tell
One of the Angels please to give
The world a push, and it
Would roll away, away, away...
(I wouldn't care a bit!)
O! But I'm glad, dear God, that You
ARe not as I would be
If I were You—You are so good,
So kind and good to me!

A GOOD WAY

LET'S see, dear God, I want to tell
You in a brand new way
"I love You!" But I cannot think
Of anything to say.
I know, dear God! I'll run and do
Something for someone, and
Then when You see me doing it
Of course You'll understand!

MAYBE

SOMETIMES, when I kneel down to pray,
I can't think of a thing to say,
And God seems—O! So far away!
And then I wish that I could see
Him just as well as He sees me—
O! Think how lovely that would be!
But if I'm good, and if I grow
Up loving Him, I will, I know,
At last go where the Angels go.
Then I will run to God, and He
Will take me up upon His knee
(At least I think He will...maybe...)
I really think He will be glad
To have me if I've not been bad
Here on the world and made Him sad.
So I will sit there on God's knee,
And He will keep His arms 'round me—
(At least I *think* He will...maybe...)

THE VERY TIME

I USED to think, if I'd been bad,
I'd better stay away
From You, dear God, I used to think
I might as well not pray.
I used to think, if I'd been bad,
You wouldn't want me to—
And so I didn't pray, but now
Of course I always do.
Now when I have been bad, dear God,
I always quickly fall
Down on my knees for then—O! then
I need You most of all!

ANGELS

DEAR God, I'm sure the Angels keep
Their arms around me while I sleep!
For sometimes, when I wake at night—
Yes, when my eyes are still shut tight—
I hear all sorts of little things
That sound just like an Angel's wings!
It wouldn't be a great surprise
If, when I did open my eyes,
I saw an Angel by the bed
And touched the halo 'round his head!

NOT UNLESS...

DEAR God I wish—I wish I could
Get suddenly so good, so good
That even all the Saints would be
Astonished when they looked at me!
But O! I know—O yes, I know
There is no use in wishing so
Unless I try, day after day,
To do what's right in every way.
Then maybe, if I try and try,
Maybe at last—before I die—
I will be nearly what I should?
O God, I wish—I *wish* I would!

THE CHILD ON HIS KNEES

IN THE MORNING

EACH morning when I wake I say
"Take all of me, dear God, today!"
I give You all I am, although
That isn't much, dear God, I know—
But still I say "Take all of me!"
I have no more to give, You see.

EXCUSES

O GOD, why am I ever bad
When I know that it makes You sad?
And O! Why don't I always do
The things that You have told me to?
Dear God, dear God, I'm very small—
But that is no excuse at all.

WAITING

O! IF I could be sure
Each day I love You more
Than any other day
That's ever been before!
O! If I could be sure
Each day I come more near
To You, dear God, than I
Have every come down here!
O! If I only could
Be sure, quite sure that I
Will give You all You want
From me before I die!
O God, I wish I knew
If You are pleased with me?
The only thing to do
Is just to wait and see.

THE CHILD ON HIS KNEES

TELL ME WHAT?

I WANT to do so much for You,
Dear God, I want to be
One of the people that You choose
To do Your work. Ask me!
O! Please don't ever be afraid,
Dear God, to ask me to
Do what is hard, for that is just
What I would *like* to do!

REMIND ME

DEAR God, dear God, if ever I
Forget You here, before I die—
O! Please remind me right away
So that I will kneel down and say
"Forgive me, God! I love You yet!"
(But O! I hope I *won't* forget).

YOUR FRIENDS

BECAUSE I love You, God, I love
The Saints—for what are they
But people who have loved You in
The very dearest way?
Of course I love Your friends, dear God,
And I would like to know
Them very, very well, because—
Because I love *You* so!

WHAT TO DO

WHEN any thought that isn't good
Gets in my head, I say
A little prayer, and the Bad Thought
Turns 'round and runs away!

DIFFERENT WAYS

DEAR God, I try to tell You
Through all the live-long day
"I love You!" And to say it
In every sort of way.
I say it in the morning
By jumping out of bed
Just when I ought to do it
You know, dear God, instead
Of lying there and thinking
How comfy beds can be—
For that would not be loving
You, God—but loving me!
And then I say "I love You!"
By washing as I should,
And all day long I say it
By trying to be good...
"I love You, God! I love You!"
There are as many ways
Of saying that I love You
As there are nights and days!

A PRAYER FOR SAD TIMES

DO ANYTHING You want with me,
Dear God, for I don't care
So long as You will let me love
You always, everywhere!
Do anything You want with me,
Dear God, for it is true
That everything You do is done
To bring me nearer You!

THE WRONG IDEA

SOMETIMES I really feel as if
I really was quite good!
Sometimes I really feel as if
I did all that I should!
O! Why is it so easy, God,
Sometimes, for me to make
Myself believe that I am good
When this is a mistake?

HOW TO TURN FUN INTO PRAYERS

YOU know I try, dear God to give
You presents every day—
Not only when I am at school,
But when I am at play.
Not only when I'm doing things
That I am made to do,
But when I'm having fun—O! Then
I give You presents too!
For when I'm having fun, I say
"O thanks, dear God!" You see,
That turns the fun into a prayer
For You, dear God, from me.

THE CHILD ON HIS KNEES

FOLLOW THE LEADER

Take me, God, and make me
What I ought to be!
O! I want to please You!
But I cannot see
Always how to do it
In the nicest way
'Till You come and tell me—
So I kneel and say
"Show me how to please You
More and more, dear God!
Show me how to follow
Just where You have trod!"

SUPPOSE...

SUPPOSE, dear God, in spite of all
These prayers I really am
Not getting better? O! Suppose
I'm nothing but a sham?
Dear God, I know that You are sad
If anybody prays
And then goes off and doesn't think
Of You in other ways.
I know, dear God, that if I say
"I love You!" And then go
And do what isn't right—then You
Are sad, so sad, I know!
O! Teach me how to live for You
Each minute of the day!
Not only when I kneel and bow
My head, dear God, and pray!

THE SUREST WAY

HELP me, dear God, to follow in
Your footsteps everyday!
    Yes, even when they seem to me
    To lead a hilly way!
    O! Do not ever let me try
    A shorter cut, dear God!
    The surest way to find You is
    Along the path You trod.

TRADING

DEAR God, I know that if I loved
You very much—then I
Would do more for You than I do—
Or anyway, I'd try!
O! Teach me how to love You more,
Dear God, I want to give
You all my live, so please—O please
Do show me how to live!

THE CHILD ON HIS KNEES

REMEMBERING

HOW nice it was of You to be
A little Child, dear God!
I love to think my feet are on
The same world that You trod!